FLOWER FAIRIES™

FOUR SEASONS

FLOWER FAIRIES

FAIRIES ™

FOUR SEASONS

CICELY MARY BARKER

The reproductions in this book have been made using the most modern electronic scanning methods from entirely new transparencies of Cicely Mary Barker's original watercolours. They enable Cicely Mary Barker's skill as an artist to be appreciated as never before.

FREDERICK WARNE

Published by the Penguin Group
27 Wrights Lane, London W8 5TZ, England
Penguin Putnam Inc, 375 Hudson Street, New York, N.Y. 10014, USA
Penguin Books Australia Ltd, Ringwood, Victoria, Australia
Penguin Books Canada Ltd, 10 Alcorn Avenue, Toronto, Ontario, Canada M4V 3B2
Penguin Books (NZ) Ltd, 182-190 Wairau Road, Auckland 10, New Zealand

Penguin Books Ltd, Registered Offices: Harmondsworth, Middlesex, England

This edition first published 2003

1 3 5 7 9 10 8 6 4 2

ISBN 0 7232 4948 2

Printed in China

CONTENTS

*I*NTRODUCTION

Cicely Mary Barker was born in West
Croydon, Surrey, on 28 June 1895.
All her life she was physically frail
and as a child suffered from epilepsy.
Apart from bouts of illness, Cicely's
childhood was happy and secure.
The Barkers' were deeply religious
and Cicely herself was a devout

Cicely Mary Barker

Christian who used art to express her spiritual beliefs.
It was Cicely's father, an accomplished artist himself,
who encouraged her artistic talent, enrolling her at
Croydon Art Society when she was thirteen years old
and paying for a correspondence course in art which
she continued until 1919.

She was only sixteen when she had her first work
accepted for publication as a set of postcards, and
from that time she devoted her career to painting.
She was greatly influenced by the Pre-Raphaelites and
believed, as they did, in "truth to nature". In creating
her Flower Fairies books, she painted from life
whenever she could, sometimes enlisting the help of
staff at Kew Gardens in finding and identifying plant
specimens. The Fairies too were painted from life,

modelled on the children who attended her sister's nursery school. When the paintings were complete, she wrote the accompanying poems.

First editions of the little Flower Fairies books

The first of the seasonal Flower Fairies books, *Flower Fairies of the Spring*, was published in 1923, and was well received by the war-weary public, who were fascinated by fairies and charmed by her vision of innocence. *Flower Fairies of the Summer* came in 1925 and a year later in 1926, *Flower Fairies of the Autumn* was published. *Flower Fairies of the Winter* was a collection first published in 1985, some years after Cicely's death in 1973.

Flower Fairies Four Seasons features Flower Fairies from the current editions of Cicely Mary Barker's books, showcasing the enormous artistic talent that has enabled Cicely Mary Barker's work to survive in a more aggressively modern age and to give pleasure to so many admirers.

FLOWER
FAIRIES
OF THE
SPRING

❖

SPRING MAGIC

The World is very old;
　　But year by year
It groweth new again
　　When buds appear.

The World is very old,
　　And sometimes sad;
But when the daisies come
　　The World is glad.

The World is very old;
　　But every Spring
It groweth young again,
　　And fairies sing.

The Song of the Crocus Fairy

Crocus of yellow, new and gay;
Mauve and purple, in brave array;
Crocus white
Like a cup of light,—
Hundreds of them are smiling up,
Each with a flame in its shining cup,
By the touch of the warm and welcome sun
Opened suddenly. Spring's begun!
Dance then, fairies, for joy, and sing
The song of the coming again of Spring.

The Song of
the Colt's-Foot Fairy

The winds of March are keen and cold;
I fear them not, for I am bold.

I wait not for my leaves to grow;
They follow after: they are slow.

My yellow blooms are brave and bright;
I greet the Spring with all my might.

THE SONG OF
THE CELANDINE FAIRY

Before the hawthorn leaves unfold,
Or buttercups put forth their gold,
By every sunny footpath shine
The stars of Lesser Celandine.

The Song of the Willow-Catkin Fairy

The people call me Palm, they do;
They call me Pussy-willow too.
And when I'm full in bloom, the bees
Come humming round my yellow trees.

The people trample round about
And spoil the little trees, and shout;
My shiny twigs are thin and brown:
The people pull and break them down.

To keep a Holy Feast, they say,
They take my pretty boughs away.
I should be glad—I should not mind—
If only people weren't unkind.

Oh, you may pick a piece, you may
(So dear and silky, soft and grey);
But if you're rough and greedy, why
You'll make the little fairies cry.

(This catkin is the flower of the Sallow Willow.)

The Song of the Windflower Fairy

While human-folk slumber,
  The fairies espy
Stars without number
  Sprinkling the sky.

The Winter's long sleeping,
  Like night-time, is done;
But day-stars are leaping
  To welcome the sun.

Star-like they sprinkle
  The wildwood with light;
Countless they twinkle—
  The Windflowers white!

("Windflower" is another name for
Wood Anemone.)

The Song of
the Daisy Fairy

Come to me and play with me,
　　I'm the babies' flower;
Make a necklace gay with me,
Spend the whole long day with me,
　　Till the sunset hour.

I must say Good-night, you know,
　　Till tomorrow's playtime;
Close my petals tight, you know,
Shut the red and white, you know,
　　Sleeping till the daytime.

The Song of the Dandelion Fairy

Here's the Dandelion's rhyme:
   See my leaves with tooth-like edges;
Blow my clocks to tell the time;
   See me flaunting by the hedges,
In the meadow, in the lane,
   Gay and naughty in the garden;
Pull me up—I grow again,
   Asking neither leave nor pardon.
Sillies, what are you about
   With your spades and hoes of iron?
You can never drive me out—
   Me, the dauntless Dandelion!

THE SONG OF
THE DAFFODIL FAIRY

I'm everyone's darling: the blackbird and
    starling
Are shouting about me from blossoming
    boughs;
For I, the Lent Lily, the Daffy-down-dilly,
Have heard through the country the call to
    arouse.
The orchards are ringing with voices
    a-singing
The praise of my petticoat, praise of my
    gown;
The children are playing, and hark! they are
    saying
That Daffy-down-dilly is come up to town!

The Song of
the Dog-Violet Fairy

The wren and robin hop around;
    The Primrose-maids my neighbours be;
The sun has warmed the mossy ground;
Where Spring has come, I too am found:
    The Cuckoo's call has wakened me!

The Song of
the Primrose Fairy

The Primrose opens wide in spring;
    Her scent is sweet and good:
It smells of every happy thing
    In sunny lane and wood.
I have not half the skill to sing
    And praise her as I should.

She's dear to folk throughout the land;
    In her is nothing mean:
She freely spreads on every hand
    Her petals pale and clean.
And though she's neither proud nor grand,
    She is the Country Queen.

The Song of
the Lady's-Smock Fairy

Where the grass is damp and green,
Where the shallow streams are flowing,
Where the cowslip buds are showing,
   I am seen.

Dainty as a fairy's frock,
White or mauve, of elfin sewing,
'Tis the meadow-maiden growing—
   Lady's-smock.

The Song of
the Larch Fairy

Sing a song of Larch trees
    Loved by fairy-folk;
Dark stands the pinewood,
    Bare stands the oak,
But the Larch is dressed and trimmed
    Fit for fairy-folk!

Sing a song of Larch trees,
    Sprays that swing aloft,
Pink tufts, and tassels
    Grass-green and soft:
All to please the little elves
    Singing songs aloft!

The Song of
the Bluebell Fairy

My hundred thousand bells of blue,
    The splendour of the Spring,
They carpet all the woods anew
With royalty of sapphire hue;
The Primrose is the Queen, 'tis true.
    But surely I am King!
       Ah yes,
    The peerless Woodland King!

Loud, loud the thrushes sing their song;
    The bluebell woods are wide;
My stems are tall and straight and strong;
From ugly streets the children throng,
They gather armfuls, great and long,
    Then home they troop in pride—
       Ah yes,
    With laughter and with pride!

(This is the Wild Hyacinth. The Bluebell of Scotland
is the Harebell.)

The Song of the Stitchwort Fairy

I am brittle-stemmed and slender,
But the grass is my defender.

On the banks where grass is long,
I can stand erect and strong.

All my mass of starry faces
Looking up from wayside places,

From the thick and tangled grass,
Gives you greeting as you pass.

(A prettier name for Stitchwort is
Starwort, but it is not so often used.)

The
Stitchwort
Fairy.

The Song of the Wood-Sorrel Fairy

In the wood the trees are tall,
 Up and up they tower;
You and I are very small—
 Fairy-child and flower.

Bracken stalks are shooting high,
 Far and far above us;
We are little, you and I,
 But the fairies love us.

THE SONG OF
THE SPEEDWELL FAIRY

Clear blue are the skies;
　　My petals are blue;
　　As beautiful, too,
As bluest of eyes.

The heavens are high:
　　By the field-path I grow
　　Where wayfarers go,
And "Good speed," say I;

"See, here is a prize
　　Of wonderful worth:
　　A weed of the earth,
As blue as the skies!"

(There are many kinds of
Speedwell: this is the Germander.)

The Song of the Lords-and-Ladies Fairy

Here's the song of Lords-and-Ladies
  (in the damp and shade he grows):
I have neither bells nor petals,
  like the foxglove or the rose.
Through the length and breadth of England,
  many flowers you may see—
Petals, bells, and cups in plenty—
  but there's no one else like me.

In the hot-house dwells my kinsman,
  Arum-lily, white and fine;
I am not so tall and stately,
  but the quaintest hood is mine;
And my glossy leaves are handsome;
  I've a spike to make you stare;
And my berries are a glory in September.
  (BUT BEWARE!)

(The Wild Arum has other names beside
Lords-and-/Ladies, such as Cuckoo-pint and
Jack-in-the-Pulpit.)

The Song of
the Cowslip Fairy

The land is full of happy birds
And flocks of sheep and grazing herds.

I hear the songs of larks that fly
Above me in the breezy sky.

I hear the little lambkins bleat;
My honey-scent is rich and sweet.

Beneath the sun I dance and play
In April and in merry May.

The grass is green as green can be;
The children shout at sight of me.

The Song of
the Heart's-Ease Fairy

Like the richest velvet
    (I've heard the fairies tell)
Grow the handsome pansies
    within the garden wall;
When you praise their beauty,
    remember me as well—
Think of little Heart's-ease,
    the brother of them all!

Come away and seek me
    when the year is young,
Through the open ploughlands
    beyond the garden wall;
Many names are pretty
    and many songs are sung:
Mine—because I'm Heart's-ease—
    are prettiest of all!

(An old lady says that when she was a little
girl the children's name for the Heart's-ease
or Wild Pansy was Jump-up-and-kiss-me!)

The Song of
the May Fairy

My buds, they cluster small and green;
   The sunshine gaineth heat:
Soon shall the hawthorn tree be clothed
   As with a snowy sheet.

O magic sight, the hedge is white,
   My scent is very sweet;
And lo, where I am come indeed,
   The Spring and Summer meet.

FLOWER
FAIRIES
OF THE
SUMMER

❖

Spring Goes,
Summer Comes

The little darling, Spring,
    Has run away;
The sunshine grew too hot for her to stay.

She kissed her sister, Summer,
    And she said:
"When I am gone, you must be queen
    instead."

Now reigns the Lady Summer,
    Round whose feet
A thousand fairies flock with blossoms sweet.

PLANTAIN AND MOON-DAISY DANCING TOGETHER,
ALL THROUGH THE BEAUTIFUL SUNSHINY WEATHER

The Song of
the Buttercup Fairy

'Tis I whom children love the best;
   My wealth is all for them;
For them is set each glossy cup
   Upon each sturdy stem.

O little playmates whom I love!
   The sky is summer-blue,
And meadows full of buttercups
   Are spread abroad for you.

THE SONG OF
THE HERB ROBERT FAIRY

Little Herb Robert,
    Bright and small,
Peeps from the bank
    Or the old stone wall.

Little Herb Robert,
    His leaf turns red;
He's wild geranium,
    So it is said.

The Song of the Forget-me-not Fairy

So small, so blue, in grassy places
    My flowers raise
    Their tiny faces.

By streams my bigger sisters grow,
    And smile in gardens,
    In a row.

I've never seen a garden plot;
    But though I'm small
    Forget me not!

The Song of the Poppy Fairy

The green wheat's a-growing,
    The lark sings on high;
In scarlet silk a-glowing,
    Here stand I.

The wheat's turning yellow,
    Ripening for sheaves;
I hear the little fellow
    Who scares the bird-thieves.

Now the harvest's ended,
    The wheat-field is bare;
But still, red and splendid,
    I am there.

The Song of
the Foxglove Fairy

"Foxglove, Foxglove,
　　What do you see?"
The cool green woodland,
　　The fat velvet bee;
Hey, Mr Bumble,
　　I've honey here for thee!

"Foxglove, Foxglove,
　　What see you now?"
The soft summer moonlight
　　On bracken, grass, and bough;
And all the fairies dancing
　　As only they know how.

THE SONG OF THE WILD ROSE FAIRY

I am the queen whom everybody knows:
    I am the English Rose;
As light and free as any Jenny Wren,
    As dear to Englishmen;
As joyous as a Robin Redbreast's tune,
    I scent the air of June;
My buds are rosy as a baby's cheek;
    I have one word to speak,
One word which is my secret and my song,
'Tis "England, England, England" all day long.

The Song of
the White Clover Fairy

I'm little White Clover, kind and clean;
Look at my threefold leaves so green;
Hark to the buzzing of hungry bees:
"Give us your honey, Clover, please!"

Yes, little bees, and welcome, too!
My honey is good, and meant for you!

The Song of the Honeysuckle Fairy

The lane is deep, the bank is steep,
   The tangled hedge is high;
And clinging, twisting, up I creep,
   And climb towards the sky.
O Honeysuckle, mounting high!
O Woodbine, climbing to the sky!

The people in the lane below
   Look up and see me there,
Where I my honey-trumpets blow,
   Whose sweetness fills the air.
O Honeysuckle, waving there!
O Woodbine, scenting all the air!

The Song of the Bird's-foot Trefoil Fairy

Here I dance in a dress like flames,
And laugh to think of my comical names.
Hoppetty hop, with nimble legs!
Some folks call me *Bacon and Eggs*!
While other people, it's really true,
Tell me I'm *Cuckoo's Stockings* too!
Over the hill I skip and prance;
I'm *Lady's Slipper*, and so I dance,
Not like a lady, grand and proud,
But to the grasshoppers' chirping loud.
My pods are shaped like a dicky's toes:
That is what *Bird's-Foot Trefoil* shows;
This is my name which grown–ups use,
But children may call me what they choose.

The Song of
the Nightshade Fairy

My name is Nightshade, also Bittersweet;
    Ah, little folk, be wise!
Hide you your hands behind you when we meet,
    Turn you away your eyes.
My flowers you shall not pick, nor berries eat,
    For in them poison lies.

(Though this is so poisonous, it is not the
Deadly Nightshade, but the Woody Nightshade.
The berries turn red a little later on.)

THE SONG OF
THE HAREBELL FAIRY

O bells, on stems so thin and fine!
   No human ear
   Your sound can hear,
O lightly chiming bells of mine!

When dim and dewy twilight falls,
   Then comes the time
   When harebells chime
For fairy feasts and fairy balls.

They tinkle while the fairies play,
   With dance and song,
   The whole night long,
Till daybreak wakens, cold and grey,
And elfin music fades away.

(The Harebell is the Bluebell of Scotland.)

The Song of
the Heather Fairy

"Ho, Heather, ho! From south to north
Spread now your royal purple forth!
Ho, jolly one! From east to west,
The moorland waiteth to be dressed!"

I come, I come! With footsteps sure
I run to clothe the waiting moor;
From heath to heath I leap and stride
To fling my bounty far and wide.

(The heather in the picture is bell heather,
or heath; it is different from the common
heather which is also called ling.)

THE SONG OF
THE YARROW FAIRY

Among the harebells and the grass,
   The grass all feathery with seed,
I dream, and see the people pass:
   They pay me little heed.

And yet the children (so I think)
   In spite of other flowers more dear,
Would miss my clusters white and pink,
   If I should disappear.

(The Yarrow has another name, Milfoil, which
means Thousand Leaf; because her leaves are
all made up of very many tiny little leaves.)

THE SONG OF
THE TOADFLAX FAIRY

The children, the children,
   they call me funny names,
They take me for their darling
   and partner in their games;
They pinch my flowers' yellow mouths,
   to open them and close,
Saying, *Snap-Dragon!*
     Toadflax!
       or, *darling Bunny-Nose!*

The Toadflax, the Toadflax,
   with lemon-coloured spikes,
With funny friendly faces
   that everybody likes,
Upon the grassy hillside
   and hedgerow bank it grows,
And it's *Snap-Dragon!*
     Toadflax!
       and *darling Bunny-Nose!*

THE SONG OF
THE SCABIOUS FAIRY

Like frilly cushions full of pins
For tiny dames and fairykins;

Or else like dancers decked with gems,
My flowers sway on slender stems.

They curtsey in the meadow grass,
And nod to butterflies who pass.

The Song of the Scarlet Pimpernel Fairy

By the furrowed fields I lie,
Calling to the passers-by:
"If the weather you would tell,
Look at Scarlet Pimpernel."

When the day is warm and fine,
I unfold these flowers of mine;
Ah, but you must look for rain
When I shut them up again!

Weather-glasses on the walls
Hang in wealthy people's halls:
Though I lie where cart-wheels pass
I'm the Poor Man's Weather-Glass!

The Song of the
Greater Knapweed Fairy

Oh, please, little children, take note of my
    name:
To call me a thistle is really a shame:
I'm harmless old Knapweed, who grows
    on the chalk,
I never will prick you when out for your
    walk.

Yet I should be sorry, yes, sorry indeed,
To cut your small fingers and cause them
    to bleed;
So bid me Good Morning when out for
    your walk,
And mind how you pull at my very tough
    stalk.

(Sometimes this Knapweed is called Hardhead;
and he has a brother, the little Knapweed, whose
flower is not quite like this.)

The Song of the Traveller's Joy Fairy

Traveller, traveller, tramping by
To the seaport town where the big ships lie,
See, I have built a shady bower
To shelter you from the sun or shower.
Rest for a bit, then on, my boy!
Luck go with you, and Traveller's Joy!

Traveller, traveller, tramping home
From foreign places beyond the foam,
See, I have hung out a white festoon
To greet the lad with the dusty shoon.
Somewhere a lass looks out for a boy:
Luck be with you, and Traveller's Joy!

(Traveller's Joy is Wild Clematis; and when the flowers
are over, it becomes a mass of silky fluff, and then
we call it Old-Man's-Beard.)

The Song of
the Ragwort Fairy

Now is the prime of Summer past,
 Farewell she soon must say;
But yet my gold you may behold
 By every grassy way.

And what though Autumn comes apace,
 And brings a shorter day?
Still stand I here, your eyes to cheer,
 In gallant gold array.

The Song of the Rose Fairy

Best and dearest flower that grows,
Perfect both to see and smell;
Words can never, never tell
Half the beauty of a Rose—
Buds that open to disclose
Fold on fold of purest white,
Lovely pink, or red that glows
Deep, sweet-scented. What delight
  To be Fairy of the Rose!

FLOWER
FAIRIES
OF THE
AUTUMN

With the nuts and berries they bring

❖

AUTUMN

SEE ABOVE THE FAIRY'S
HEAD, GUELDER·ROSE'S
BERRIES RED.

The Berry-Queen

An elfin rout,
    With berries laden,
Throngs round about
    A merry maiden.

Red-gold her gown;
    Sun-tanned is she;
She wears a crown
    Of bryony.

The sweet Spring came,
    And lovely Summer:
Guess, then, her name—
    This latest-comer!

The Song of
the Mountain Ash Fairy

They thought me, once, a magic tree
    Of wondrous lucky charm,
And at the door they planted me
    To keep the house from harm.

They have no fear of witchcraft now,
    Yet here am I today;
I've hung my berries from the bough,
    And merrily I say:

"Come, all you blackbirds, bring your wives,
    Your sons and daughters too;
The finest banquet of your lives
    Is here prepared for you."

(The Mountain Ash's other name is Rowan; and
it used to be called Witchentree and Witch-wood too.)

The Song of
the Michaelmas Daisy Fairy

"Red Admiral, Red Admiral,
   I'm glad to see you here,
      Alighting on my daisies one by one!
I hope you like their flavour
   and although the Autumn's near,
      Are happy as you sit there in the sun?"

"I thank you very kindly, sir!
   Your daisies *are* so nice,
      So pretty and so plentiful are they;
The flavour of their honey, sir,
   it really does entice;
      I'd like to bring my brothers, if I may!"

"Friend butterfly, friend butterfly,
   go fetch them one and all!
      I'm waiting here to welcome every guest;
And tell them it is Michaelmas,
   and soon the leaves will fall,
      But *I* think Autumn sunshine is the best!"

The Song of
the Wayfaring Tree Fairy

My shoots are tipped with buds as dusty-grey
As ancient pilgrims toiling on their way.

Like Thursday's child with far to go, I stand,
All ready for the road to Fairyland;

With hood, and bag, and shoes, my name to suit,
And in my hand my gorgeous-tinted fruit.

The Song of
the Robin's Pincushion Fairy

People come and look at me,
Asking who this rogue may be?
—Up to mischief, they suppose,
Perched upon the briar-rose.

I am nothing else at all
But a fuzzy-wuzzy ball,
Like a little bunch of flame;
I will tell you how I came:

First there came a naughty fly,
Pricked the rose, and made her cry;
Out I popped to see about it;
This is true, so do not doubt it!

THE SONG OF
THE ELDERBERRY FAIRY

Tread quietly:
O people, hush!
—For don't you see
A spotted thrush,
One thrush or two,
Or even three,
In every laden elder-tree?

They pull and lug,
They flap and push,
They peck and tug
To strip the bush;
They have forsaken
Snail and slug;
Unseen I watch them, safe and snug!

(These berries do us no harm, though they don't
taste very nice. Country people make wine from
them; and boys make whistles from elder stems.)

The Song of the Acorn Fairy

To English folk the mighty oak
    Is England's noblest tree;
Its hard-grained wood is strong and good
    As English hearts can be.
And would you know how oak-trees grow,
    The secret may be told:
You do but need to plant for seed
    One acorn in the mould;
For even so, long years ago,
    Were born the oaks of old.

THE SONG OF
THE DOGWOOD FAIRY

I was a warrior,
    When, long ago,
Arrows of Dogwood
    Flew from the bow.
Passers-by, nowadays,
    Go up and down,
Not one remembering
    My old renown.

Yet when the Autumn sun
    Colours the trees,
Should you come seeking me,
    Know me by these:
Bronze leaves and crimson leaves,
    Soon to be shed;
Dark little berries,
    On stalks turning red.

(Cornel is another name for Dogwood; and Dogwood
has nothing to do with dogs. It used to be Dag-wood, or
Dagger-wood, which, with another name, Prickwood,
show that it was used to make sharp-pointed things.)

The Song of
the Black Bryony Fairy

Bright and wild and beautiful
For the Autumn festival,
I will hang from tree to tree
Wreaths and ropes of Bryony,
To the glory and the praise
Of the sweet September days.

(There is nothing black to be seen about this Bryony,
but people do say it has a black root; and this may
be true, but you would need to dig it up to find out.
It used to be thought a cure for freckles.)

The Song of
the Horse Chestnut Fairy

My conkers, they are shiny things,
  And things of mighty joy,
And they are like the wealth of kings
  To every little boy;
I see the upturned face of each
  Who stands around the tree:
He sees his treasure out of reach,
  But does not notice *me*.

For love of conkers bright and brown,
  He pelts the tree all day;
With stones and sticks he knocks them down,
  And thinks it jolly play.
But sometimes I, the elf, am hit
  Until I'm black and blue;
O laddies, only wait a bit,
  I'll shake them down to you!

The Song of the Blackberry Fairy

My berries cluster black and thick
For rich and poor alike to pick.

I'll tear your dress, and cling, and tease,
And scratch your hands and arms and knees.

I'll stain your fingers and your face,
And then I'll laugh at your disgrace.

But when the bramble-jelly's made,
You'll find your trouble well repaid.

THE SONG OF
THE NIGHTSHADE BERRY FAIRY

"You see my berries, how they gleam and
    glow,
Clear ruby-red, and green, and orange-
    yellow;
Do they not tempt you, fairies, dangling so?"
   The fairies shake their heads and answer "No!
    You are a crafty fellow!"

"What, won't you try them? There is
    naught to pay!
Why should you think my berries poisoned
    things?
You fairies may look scared and fly away—
The children will believe me when I say
    My fruit is fruit for kings!"
   But all good fairies cry in anxious haste,
"O children, do not taste!"

(You must believe the good fairies, though the berries
look nice. This is the Woody Nightshade, which has
purple and yellow flowers in the summer.)

The Song of the Rose Hip Fairy

Cool dewy morning,
    Blue sky at noon,
White mist at evening,
    And large yellow moon;

Blackberries juicy
    For staining of lips;
And scarlet, O scarlet
    The Wild Rose Hips!

Gay as a gipsy
    All Autumn long,
Here on the hedge-top
    This is my song.

The Song of
the Crab-Apple Fairy

Crab-apples, Crab-apples, out in the wood,
Little and bitter, yet little and good!
The apples in orchards, so rosy and fine,
Are children of wild little apples like mine.

The branches are laden, and droop to the
              ground;
The fairy-fruit falls in a circle around;
Now all you good children, come gather
              them up:
They'll make you sweet jelly to spread
              when you sup.

One little apple I'll catch for myself;
I'll stew it, and strain it, to store on a shelf
In four or five acorn-cups, locked with a key
In a cupboard of mine at the root of the tree.

The Song of
the Hazel-Nut Fairy

Slowly, slowly, growing
   While I watched them well,
See, my nuts have ripened;
   Now I've news to tell.
I will tell the Squirrel,
   "Here's a store for you;
But, kind Sir, remember
   The Nuthatch likes them too."

I will tell the Nuthatch,
   "Now, Sir, you may come;
Choose your nuts and crack them,
   But leave the children some."
I will tell the children,
   "You may take your share;
Come and fill your pockets,
   But leave a few to spare."

The Song of
the White Bryony Fairy

Have you seen at Autumn-time
　　Fairy-folk adorning
All the hedge with necklaces,
　　Early in the morning?
Green beads and red beads
　　Threaded on a vine:
Is there any handiwork
　　Prettier than mine?

(This Bryony has other names—White Vine, Wild
Vine, and Red-berried Bryony. It has tendrils to
climb with, which Black Bryony has not, and its
leaves and berries are quite different. They say its
root is white, as the other's is black.)

The Song of the Beechnut Fairy

O the great and happy Beech,
　　Glorious and tall!
Changing with the changing months,
　　Lovely in them all:

Lovely in the leafless time,
　　Lovelier in green;
Loveliest with golden leaves
　　And the sky between,

When the nuts are falling fast,
　　Thrown by little me—
Tiny things to patter down
　　From a forest tree!

(You may eat these.)

The Song of
the Hawthorn Fairy

These thorny branches bore the May
    So many months ago,
That when the scattered petals lay
    Like drifts of fallen snow,
    "This is the story's end," you said;
    But O, not half was told!
For see, my haws are here instead,
And hungry birdies shall be fed
    On these when days are cold.

The Song of
the Privet Fairy

Here in the wayside hedge I stand,
And look across the open land;
Rejoicing thus, unclipped and free,
I think how you must envy me,
O garden Privet, prim and neat,
With tidy gravel at your feet!

(In early summer the Privet has spikes of
very strongly-scented white flowers.)

THE SONG OF
THE SLOE FAIRY

When Blackthorn blossoms leap to sight,
They deck the hedge with starry light,
    In early Spring
    When rough winds blow,
    Each promising
    A purple sloe.

And now is Autumn here, and lo,
The Blackthorn bears the purple sloe!
    But ah, how much
    Too sharp these plums,
    Until the touch
    Of Winter comes!

(The sloe is a wild plum. One bite will set your
teeth on edge until it has been mellowed by frost;
but it is not poisonous.)

142

FLOWER
FAIRIES
OF THE
WINTER

❖

THE SONG OF
THE SNOWDROP FAIRY

Deep sleeps the Winter,
    Cold, wet, and grey;
Surely all the world is dead;
    Spring is far away.
Wait! the world shall waken;
    It is not dead, for lo,
The Fair Maids of February
    Stand in the snow!

The Song of the Yew Fairy

Here, on the dark and solemn Yew,
   A marvel may be seen,
Where waxen berries, pink and new,
   Appear amid the green.

I sit a-dreaming in the tree,
   So old and yet so new;
One hundred years, or two, or three
   Are little to the Yew.

I think of bygone centuries,
   And seem to see anew
The archers face their enemies
   With bended bows of Yew.

The Song of
the Winter Jasmine Fairy

All through the Summer my leaves were
green,
But never a flower of mine was seen;
Now Summer is gone, that was so gay,
And my little green leaves are shed away.
      In the grey of the year
      What cheer, what cheer?

The Winter is come, the cold winds blow;
I shall feel the frost and the drifting snow;
But the sun can shine in December too,
And this is the time of my gift to you.
      See here, see here,
      My flowers appear!

The swallows have flown beyond the sea,
But friendly Robin, he stays with me;
And little Tom-Tit, so busy and small,
Hops where the jasmine is thick on the wall;
      And we say: "Good cheer!
      We're here! We're here!"

THE SONG OF
THE DEAD-NETTLE FAIRY

Through sun and rain, the country lane,
The field, the road, are my abode.
Though leaf and bud be splashed with mud,
Who cares? Not I!—I see the sky,
The kindly sun, the wayside fun
Of tramping folk who smoke and joke,
The bairns who heed my dusty weed
(No sting have I to make them cry),
And truth to tell, they love me well.
My brothers, White, and Yellow bright,
Are finer chaps than I, perhaps;
Who cares? Not I! So now good-bye.

The Song of the Rush-Grass and Cotton-Grass Fairies

Safe across the moorland
    Travellers may go,
If they heed our warning—
    We're the ones who know!

Let the footpath guide you—
    You'll be safely led;
There is bog beside you
    Where you cannot tread!

Mind where you are going!
    If you turn aside
Where you see us growing,
    Trouble will betide.

Keep you to the path, then!
    Hark to what we say!
Else, into the quagmire
    You will surely stray.

The Song of
the Spindle Berry Fairy

See the rosy-berried Spindle
All to sunset colours turning,
Till the thicket seems to kindle,
Just as though the trees were burning.
While my berries split and show
Orange-coloured seeds aglow,
One by one my leaves must fall:
Soon the wind will take them all.
Soon must fairies shut their eyes
For the Winter's hushabies;
But, before the Autumn goes,
Spindle turns to flame and rose!

THE SONG OF
THE SHEPHERD'S-PURSE FAIRY

Though I'm poor to human eyes
Really I am rich and wise.
Every tiny flower I shed
Leaves a heart-shaped purse instead.

In each purse is wealth indeed—
Every coin a living seed.
Sow the seed upon the earth—
Living plants shall spring to birth.

Silly people's purses hold
Lifeless silver, clinking gold;
But you cannot grow a pound
From a farthing in the ground.

Money may become a curse:
Give me then my Shepherd's Purse.

THE SONG OF
THE GROUNDSEL FAIRY

If dicky-birds should buy and sell
In tiny markets, I can tell
   The way they'd spend their money.
They'd ask the price of cherries sweet,
They'd choose the pinkest worms for meat,
And common Groundsel for a treat,
   Though *you* might think it funny.

Love me not, or love me well;
That's the way they'd buy and sell.

The Song of the Lords-and-Ladies Fairy

Fairies, when you lose your way,
  From the dance returning,
In the darkest undergrowth
  See my candles burning!
These shall make the pathway plain
Homeward to your beds again.

(These are the berries of the Wild Arum, which has many
other names, and has a flower like a hood in the Spring.
The berries are not to be eaten.)

The Song of
the Plane Tree Fairy

You will not find him in the wood,
    Nor in the country lane;
But in the city's parks and streets
    You'll see the Plane.

O turn your eyes from pavements grey,
    And look you up instead,
To where the Plane tree's pretty balls
    Hang overhead!

When he has shed his golden leaves,
    His balls will yet remain,
To deck the tree until the Spring
    Comes back again!

THE SONG OF
THE BURDOCK FAIRY

Wee little hooks on each brown little bur,
(Mind where you're going, O Madam and Sir!)
How they will cling to your skirt-hem and stocking!
Hear how the Burdock is laughing and mocking:
Try to get rid of me, try as you will,
Shake me and scold me, I'll stick to you still,
      I'll stick to you still!

The Song of
the Pine Tree Fairy

A tall, tall tree is the Pine tree,
    With its trunk of bright red-brown—
The red of the merry squirrels
    Who go scampering up and down.

There are cones on the tall, tall Pine tree,
    With its needles sharp and green;
Small seeds in the cones are hidden,
    And they ripen there unseen.

The elves play games with the squirrels
    At the top of the tall, tall tree,
Throwing cones for the squirrels to nibble—
    I wish I were there to see!

THE SONG OF
THE HOLLY FAIRY

O, I am green in Winter-time,
　　When other trees are brown;
Of all the trees (So saith the rhyme)
　　The holly bears the crown.
December days are drawing near
　　When I shall come to town,
And carol-boys go singing clear
Of all the trees (O hush and hear!)
　　The holly bears the crown!

For who so well-beloved and merry
As the scarlet Holly Berry?

The Song of the Box Tree Fairy

Have you seen the Box unclipped,
Never shaped and never snipped?
Often it's a garden hedge,
Just a narrow little edge;
Or in funny shapes it's cut,
And it's very pretty; *but*—

But, unclipped, it is a tree,
Growing as it likes to be;
And it has its blossoms too;
Tiny buds, the Winter through,
Wait to open in the Spring
In a scented yellow ring.

And among its leaves there play
Little blue-tits, brisk and gay.

THE SONG OF THE OLD-MAN'S-BEARD FAIRY

This is where the little elves
Cuddle down to hide themselves;
Into fluffy beds they creep,
Say good-night, and go to sleep.

(Old-Man's Beard is Wild Clematis; its flowers
are called Traveller's Joy. This silky fluff
belongs to the seeds.)

The Song of
the Blackthorn Fairy

The wind is cold, the Spring seems long
    a-waking;
  The woods are brown and bare;
Yet this is March: soon April will be making
    All things most sweet and fair.

See, even now, in hedge and thicket tangled,
    One brave and cheering sight:
The leafless branches of the Blackthorn,
    spangled
  With starry blossoms white!

(The cold days of March are sometimes called
"Blackthorn Winter".)

The Song of
the Hazel-Catkin Fairy

Like little tails of little lambs,
　　On leafless twigs my catkins swing;
They dingle-dangle merrily
　　Before the wakening of Spring.

Beside the pollen-laden tails
　　My tiny crimson tufts you see
The promise of the autumn nuts
　　Upon the slender hazel tree.

While yet the woods lie grey and still
　　I give my tidings: "Spring is near!"
One day the land shall leap to life
　　With fairies calling: "Spring is HERE!"

The
Hazel~Catkin
Fairy.

The Song of the Totter-Grass Fairy

The leaves on the tree-tops
    Dance in the breeze;
Totter-grass dances
    And sways like the trees—

Shaking and quaking!
    While through it there goes,
Dancing, a Fairy,
    On lightest of toes.

(Totter-grass is also called Quaking-grass.)

The Song of
the Winter Aconite Fairy

Deep in the earth
    I woke, I stirred.
I said: "Was that the Spring I heard?
    For something called!"
    "No, no," they said;
"Go back to sleep. Go back to bed.

    "You're far too soon;
    The world's too cold
For you, so small." So I was told.
    But how could I
    Go back to sleep?
I could not wait; I had to peep!

    Up, up, I climbed,
    And here am I.
How wide the earth! How great the sky!
    O wintry world,
    See me, awake!
Spring calls, and comes; 'tis no mistake.

The Song of the Christmas Tree Fairy

The little Christmas Tree was born
   And dwelt in open air;
It did not guess how bright a dress
   Some day its boughs would wear;
Brown cones were all, it thought, a tall
   And grown-up Fir would bear.

O little Fir! Your forest home
   Is far and far away;
And here indoors these boughs of yours
   With coloured balls are gay,
With candle-light, and tinsel bright,
   For this is Christmas Day!

A dolly-fairy stands on top,
   Till children sleep; then she
(A live one now!) from bough to bough
   Goes gliding silently.
O magic sight, this joyous night!
   O laden, sparkling tree!

INDEX

Also by Cicely Mary Barker

Flower Fairies of the Trees

Flower Fairies of the Garden

Flower Fairies of the Wayside

A Flower Fairy Alphabet